A gift for:

Jeff

From:

Mom

6 - 2008

Happy
Fatherday!

Funny Business
by Oliver Christianson a.k.a., Revilo

Copyright ©2006
Hallmark Licensing, Inc.

Published by Hallmark Books,
a division of Hallmark Cards, Inc.
Kansas City, MO 64141

Visit us on the Web at
www.Hallmark.com.

Editorial Director: Todd Hafer
Art Director: Kevin Swanson
Layout/Production: Dan Horton
With special thanks to Russ Ediger.

ISBN: 1-59530-134-8
Printed and bound in China.
BOK2069

For:
Sylvia and Zoë

Foreword

Many of our mothers have told us to always try to see the best in others, so that people will like us. A lot of folks heed that advice throughout their lives and form a group called "The Grown-ups." The rest of us become cartoonists.

Thank goodness that Revilo is one of us. His clean, disciplined artwork and bone-dry wit are a perfect mixture of civility and anarchy. With just the right combination of warmth, understanding, and insane cruelty, Revilo has produced this collection of business cartoons that ought to be taped on every employment manual, cubicle wall, coffee-room refrigerator – and supervisor's back – in the country.

Read these cartoons. Share them. Love them.

Jerry Scott
creator of *Baby Blues* and *Zits*

THE DAY THE BALLOONS DISAPPEARED

THE BEAN COUNTER'S FINAL EXAM

Kind Boss

Thoughtful Boss

Sensitive Boss

Generous Boss

Happy Boss

Patient Boss

BUSINESS 101

IF YOUR BUSINESS HAS A WAITING ROOM,
IT'S A GOOD IDEA TO HAVE MAGAZINES TO READ.
OH, AND CHAIRS. PEOPLE LIKE TO SIT IN CHAIRS
WHILE THEY READ MAGAZINES.

TIMELESS BUSINESS ADVICE

TRAVELING FOR BUSINESS:
NOT ALWAYS AS GLAMOROUS AS ONE MIGHT IMAGINE.

FABULOUS IDWA 1-35

DES MOINES 1-35

7:40 PM

REViLo

The very last person left
at the carbon paper manufacturer.

REVILO

Mid-life career changes often bring out
sides of us we never knew existed.

I FINALLY FOUND A CAREER WHICH
PERFECTLY MATCHES MY SKILLS.

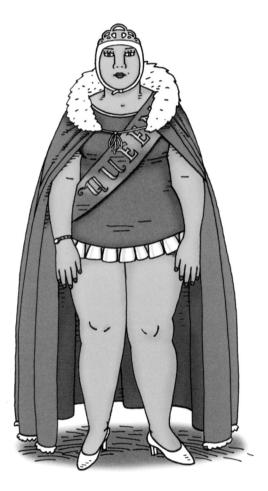

REAL LiFE TRAGEDiES
#562:

The office suck-up chokes on his tie.

REAL LIFE JOB INTERVIEWS

WHEN TED BECAME
HIS OWN BOSS
HE HAD TO LEARN
TO KISS HIS OWN BUTT.

Your Core Business

SOME EMPLOYEES SEEM TO GET
INTO "CORPORATE CASUAL" DAY
MORE THAN OTHERS.

SOME PEOPLE SAY
THAT THEIR CO-WORKERS
ARE LIKE FAMILY. THESE
ARE PEOPLE WHO SHOULD
LOOK INTO CHANGING CAREERS.

DUELING CAR SALESMEN

Hey Everybody... there's some room-temperature cold cuts left in the conference room!

According to my IT person,
neither racing stripes or flame decals
will make my computer any faster.

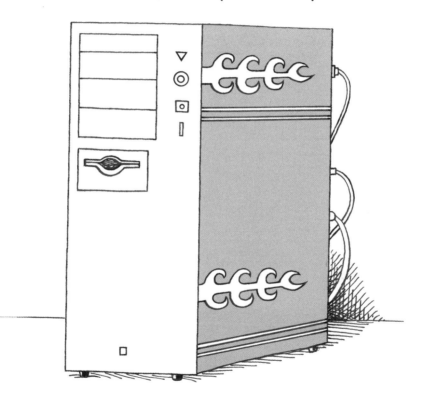

I don't know, it sure looks faster to me.

WHAT CONSULTANTS DO

The secret of doing effective presentations
is being able to remain comfortable and
confident regardless of what happens.

After a slow first quarter, Jake decided
to invest in a phone and a door
for his office.

The Foldable Laptop!

FOLDS NEATLY
TO FIT IN YOUR
BACK POCKET.

REViLo

THE TYPICAL HOME OFFICE

IMPRESS YOUR CLIENTELE WITH
FOUNDER'S PORTRAITS

Spiff up your office or work space with
a dignified portrait of some old coot!!

AS LOW AS: **$19.95**

THE BACK ROOM AT THE FLORIST

PERFECT FOR ANY MEETING!

GLAZED BAGELS

Fresh

Performance Reviews in Hell

FYI: GOOD JOBS NEVER REQUIRE YOU TO STAND ON A STREET CORNER IN A CHARACTER COSTUME IN THE SUMMER.

JOB STRESS WARNING SIGNAL #743:

RACKING UP A LOT
OF FREQUENT-FLIER
MILES WITHOUT ACTUALLY
HAVING BEEN ANYWHERE.

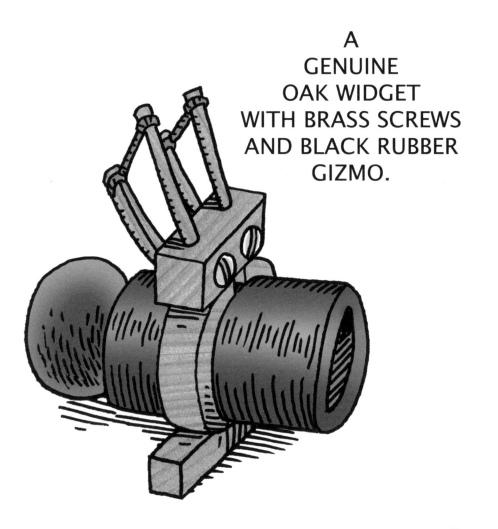

A
GENUINE
OAK WIDGET
WITH BRASS SCREWS
AND BLACK RUBBER
GIZMO.

SATURDAY NIGHT - THE CARTWRIGHTS GO TO TOWN LOOKING FOR TROUBLE.

IF YOU WORK, YOU GOTTA PLAY HARD!

Some employees can be very sensitive
about their job titles.

INTRODUCING

MALLET-TECH

LOW-TECH SOLUTIONS FOR HIGH-TECH PROBLEMS

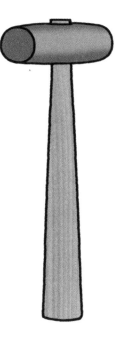

Mallet-Tech works on
all makes of computers,
copier and fax machines,
and most coin operated
coffee machines.

For Home or Office!

Save money on expensive
IT visits! Made of all natural
materials: Wood and Lead!

ONLY $ 29.95!!!!

A FLOCK OF MIGRATORY COPIER REPAIRMEN

Caffeine Helps
You Stay Focused

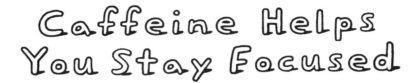

REVIL

HARRY HILLIARD LAUNCHES
A HIGHLY SUCCESSFUL TAILORING
BUSINESS BY MEETING THE SPECIAL
SARTORIAL NEEDS OF NERDS.

PROBABLY NOT A VERY GOOD PERFORMANCE REVIEW.

The point of do-it-yourself projects
is so that ordinary folks can find out why
God invented professionals.

Research and Development
is the heart and soul
of any company's future.

SANTA'S SON, SAMMY

Not quite ready to take over
the family business.

Portrait of a Self-Starter in Action

Show the World You Mean Business!

SHARK HATS

$ 19.95

available in gray only

REVILO

A STEP BY STEP GUIDE FOR DOING MOST JOBS.

1. FILL CUP WITH COFFEE. 2. DRINK COFFEE
3. FILL CUP WITH MORE COFFEE. 4. DRINK
COFFEE. 5. GO TO BATHROOM. 6. REPEAT
FIRST FOUR STEPS UNTIL LUNCH.

Understanding Corporate Thinking # 47:

management material  not so much

YOUR TACKS REFUND

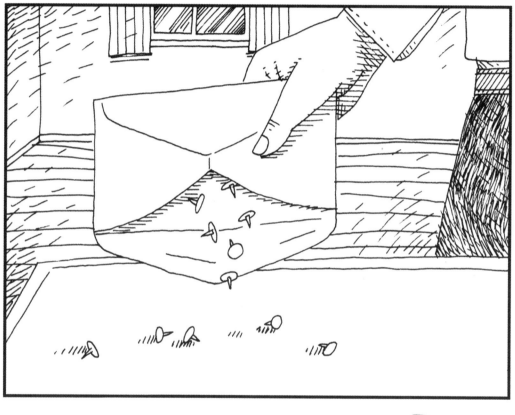

The great thing about having your own business
is that you can call it anything you damned well please.

There are many distinct advantages
to working in the home.

Some jobs are like bad marriages...

...they can get pretty hairy.

WHAT'S THE POINT OF HAVING NICE CLOTHES
IF YOU JUST DON'T KNOW HOW TO WEAR THEM?

THE ONLY FREEWAY IN HELL

THERE ARE SOME PLACES
WHERE RUSH HOUR NEVER ENDS.

Great Mysteries of the Ancient Business World

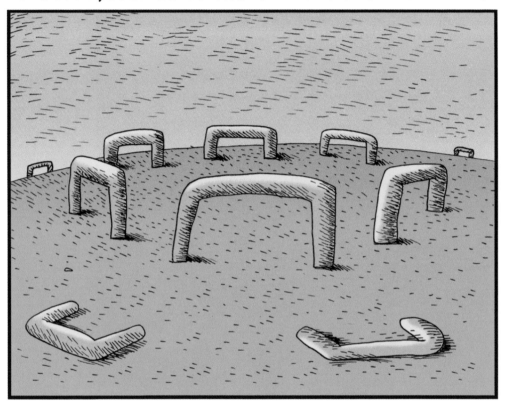

StapleHenge.

ALL YOU NEED
IS A SUIT, A TIE,
AND AN OPEN MIND.

OWNING YOUR OWN BUSINESS
ISN'T QUITE AS GLAMOROUS
AS SOME PEOPLE MIGHT IMAGINE.

LEGENDS of RETAIL

The **Mart Brothers**
Kaye, Wally and Stein

REVILO

THE MYTH OF WOMEN
IN THE BUSINESS WORLD:

TRAVEL! EXCITEMENT! GLAMOUR!

THE REALITY:
DOPEY LITTLE GREY SUITS.

BUSINESS TRAVEL

Great Moments in Business History:

In any business,
world class service is a must.

MY WORST NIGHTMARE—

I'M SKYDIVING IN THE NUDE,
AND AS I'M COMING DOWN I NOTICE
THAT ALL OF MY CO-WORKERS
ARE ON THE GROUND WATCHING,
AND AT THAT POINT I BEGIN TO FALL
MUCH MORE SLOWLY.

In any job, it's important to establish some ground rules with your employer so that he'll know that you can't be pushed around.

Talking Suits

Typical business traveler with one piece
of carry-on luggage.

If you feel you are a corporate cog,
or just someone who likes Revilo's work,
we'd like to know what you think of this collection...

Please send your comments to:
Book Feedback
2501 McGee, Mail Drop 215
Kansas City, MO 64141-6580

Or e-mail us at
booknotes@hallmark.com

P.S. If you have any messages for Revilo,
include those, too, and we'll pass them along.